# MR. MEN
## ADVENTURE IN THE
# ICE AGE

*Roger Hargreaves*

Original concept by
**Roger Hargreaves**

Written and illustrated by
**Adam Hargreaves**

Mr Snow had decided to take his friends on a fishing trip. However, Mr Snow's idea of a fishing trip was very different to what you might imagine.

Mr Snow took everyone ice fishing.

Ice fishing at the North Pole!

They knew they were there when they saw a polar bear.

The first thing they had to do when they reached the North Pole was to make a hole in the ice.

It was very thick ice.

And it was very hard work for some people.

"This is not much of a holiday," grumbled Mr Grumpy.

The fishing trip was not going well. The fish were not biting and the frost was nipping at their toes.
Everyone was freezing.

They all had red noses.

Even the walrus was a bit chilly.

Everyone except for Mr Snow, of course.

"I think it's time to go home," grumbled Mr Grumpy.

But as they set out, it began to snow.

It snowed.

And it snowed.

And it snowed.

Soon they were driving through a blizzard.

There was so much snow that the snowmobiles got stuck.

"What's that?!" cried Little Miss Helpful, suddenly.

A huge shape was lumbering towards them through the falling snow.

"Oh my goodness!" exclaimed Little Miss Helpful. "That's a …"

"… woolly mammoth!"

And, it was indeed a woolly mammoth. Mr Snow and his friends had driven into the Ice Age!

"There's only one thing to do," said Mr Snow. "We will have to ride the mammoth to safety."

Fortunately, the friendly mammoth was happy to oblige. They all climbed on to its back and set off through the snow.

"Look, there's a light in the distance," cried Little Miss Whoops, and promptly fell off the mammoth.

Luckily, the mammoth caught her with its trunk and gave her a helping hand back on board.

Or was that a helping trunk?

The light in the distance turned out to be a fire in a cave. A cave full of cavemen.

"Ugh, ugh, og," said a caveman.

Nobody knew what he was saying.

Then suddenly, Mr Clever started talking to the cavemen.
Mr Clever is so clever he could learn a new language
in five minutes flat!

They had been invited to dinner.

When they woke the next morning, it had stopped snowing, but the mammoth had wandered off in the night. How were they going to get home?

It was Mr Snow who had an idea.

He found some old mammoth tusks in the cave and using these as runners he made a large sledge.

It is very lucky that Mr Strong is very strong!

As they travelled across the vast, white landscape,
they felt totally alone.

However, they were not alone.

There was something else out there.

A something else that was hungry.

A something else that was looking for breakfast!

# A sabre-toothed tiger!

The sabre-toothed tiger came bounding through the snow after them.

"Help!" shrieked Little Miss Helpful.

Mr Strong sped up, but he could see a problem ahead.

They had reached the sea. There was nowhere to go.

They were trapped!

With his mighty strength, Mr Strong pulled the sledge to a
stop and they all stood on the ice shelf at the edge of the sea.

Then using his impressive weight, Mr Greedy jumped up
and down and broke off the ice they were standing on.

Just in the nick of time, they floated out of the reach of
the sabre-toothed tiger.

Luckily, sabre-toothed tigers can't swim!

The friends drifted through a sea of icebergs.

"It's a shame we lost our fishing rods," said Mr Snow. "We could have caught a fish."

"I don't think I want to catch an Ice Age fish," said Little Miss Scary with a shudder.

They floated on until they reached a glacier, where they could see green fields and woods below them.

They had nearly escaped the Ice Age.

But the glacier was a towering wall of ice with seemingly no way down.

It was Mr Tickle's extraordinarily long arms that came to the rescue this time.

He was able to lower everyone from one ice ledge to another until they safely reached the bottom.

They were very relieved to have left the Ice Age and much warmer.

Mr Strong was warmer.
Little Miss Helpful was warmer.
Mr Clever was warmer.
And Mr Snow was … too hot!

It had not been a very successful fishing trip.

They had not caught anything.

Except for one person.

Mr Grumpy.

He had caught a …

... cold!

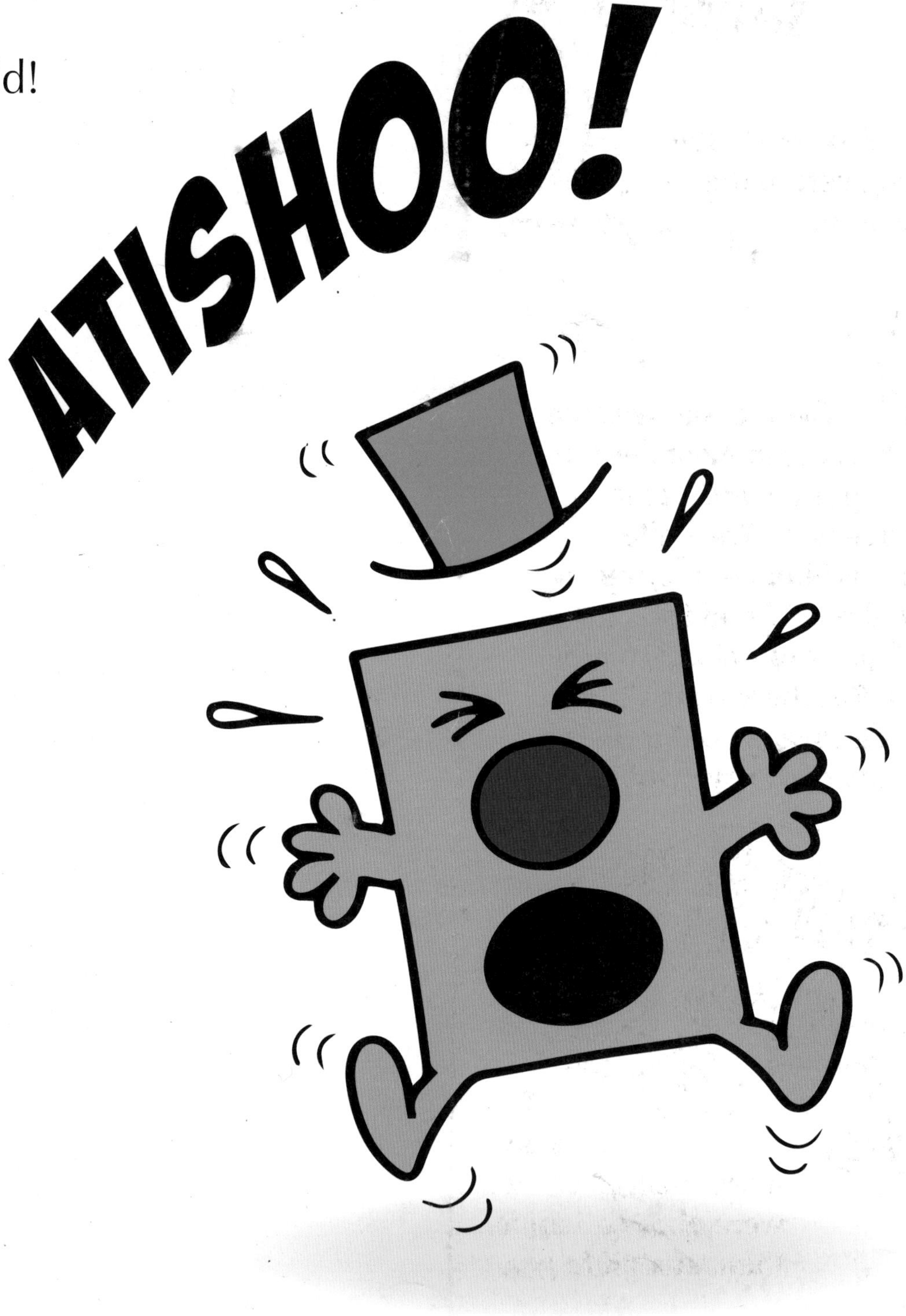